the best of christina aguilera

piano | vocal | guitar

This publication is not authorised for sale in
the United States of America and/or Canada

Wise Publications
part of The Music Sales Group
London/New York/Paris/Sydney/Copenhagen/Berlin/Madrid/Tokyo

Published by
Wise Publications
14-15 Berners Street, London W1T 3LJ, UK.

Exclusive Distributors:
Music Sales Limited
Distribution Centre, Newmarket Road,
Bury St Edmunds, Suffolk IP33 3YB
Music Sales Pty Limited
120 Rothschild Avenue, Rosebery, NSW 2018, Australia.

Order No. AM988141
ISBN 1-84609-816-5

Cover designed by Fresh Lemon.
Cover photograph courtesy of LFI.
Printed in the EU.

Beautiful

Words & Music by Linda Perry

E♭/D♭
4fr
Cm
3fr
— won - der - ful — then sud - den - ly — it's hard
- li - ri - ous, — you're so con - sumed in all your —
B
E♭
6fr
E♭/D♭
4fr
to breathe. Now and then — I get in - se - cure from all the
— doom. You're — try - ing hard — to fill the emp - ti - ness, the pie - ces
Cm
3fr
B
pain, I'm so a - shamed. —
gone, left the puz - zle un - done. That's the way it is.
A♭
4fr
Fm7
But I am beau - ti - ful — no mat - ter what — they say. —
2° you are
3° we are

E♭ 6fr
D♭ 4fr
Cm 3fr
A♭ 4fr
Words won't bring me down.
2° you
3° you
But I am beau-ti-ful in
2° You are
3° 'Cause we are
Fm7
E♭ 6fr
D♭ 4fr
Cm 3fr
ev-'ry sin-gle way.
Words won't bring me down.
2° you
3° us
Fm
To Coda
1.
E♭ 6fr
So don't you bring me down to-day.
E♭/D♭ 4fr
Cm 3fr
B

2.
E♭
6fr
E♭7/D♭
4fr
today.
(No matter what we do.)
(No matter what they say.)
Vocal ad lib.
Cm
3fr
B
(There's a song inside the tune.)
(Full of beautiful mistakes.)
E♭
6fr
E♭7/D♭
4fr
(And ev'rywhere you go.)
(The sun will always shine.)
Cm
3fr
B
D.S. al Coda
(But tomorrow we might awake
on the other side.)

Coda
E♭
6fr
E♭/D♭
4fr
to - day.
Oh.
Cm
3fr
B
E♭
6fr
To - day.
E♭/D♭
4fr
Cm
3fr
Free time
B
E♭
6fr
Don't you bring me down
to - day.
8vb

Ain't No Other Man

Words & Music by Christina Aguilera, Kara Dioguardi, DJ Premier, Charles Roane & Harold Beatty

B♭ Fm
Some-thin 'bout you caught my eye. Some-thing moved me deep in - side.
What was cloud - y now is clear. You're the light that I need-ed.
D♭7 C7
4fr 3fr
B♭ Fm
I don't know what you did boy, but you had it.
You got what I want boy and I want it.
And I've been hooked ev - er since. Told my mo-ther, my bro-ther, my
So keep on giv - ing it up. So tell your mo ther, your bro-ther, your
B♭ Fm B♭ Fm
sis - ter and my friends. Told the oth - ers, my lov - ers, both past and pre - sent tense, that
sis - ter and your friends. Tell the oth - ers, your lov - ers, bet - ter not be pre - sent tense, 'cause

B♭
Fm7
ev - 'ry time I see you ev - 'ry - thing starts mak - ing sense.
I want ev - 'ry - one to know that you are mine and no - one else - es.
Fm7
B♭
Fm
(Do your thang, hon- ey.)
Ain't no oth - er man can stand up next to you. Ain't
B♭
Fm
no oth - er man on the pla - net does what you do. You're the kin - da guy a girl finds
B♭
Fm
D♭7
4fr
C7
3fr
in a blue moon. You got soul, you got class, you got style, you bad ass.

B♭
Fm7
Ain't no oth - er man, it's true. Ain't no oth-er man but you.
1.
2.
N.C.
(Break it down now.) Ain't no oth-er, ain't,
ain't no oth - er, oth - er. Ain't no oth - er, ain't, ain't no oth - er lov - er.
Ain't no oth- er, I, I, I need no oth - er. Ain't no oth - er man but you.

D♭7
C7
4fr
3fr
You are there when I'm a mess.
Talk me down from ev - 'ry ledge.
Give me strength, boy, you're
the best.
You're the on - ly one who's ev - er passed ev - 'ry test.
B♭
Fm
Fm7
Ain't no oth - er man can stand

B♭
Fm
up next to you. Ain't no oth-er man on the pla-net does what you do. You're
the kin-da guy a girl finds in a blue moon. You got soul, you got class, you got
D♭7
C7
4fr
3fr
style, you bad ass. Ain't no oth-er man, it's true. Ain't no oth-er man but
1.
2.
you.
And now I'm tell-ing you son, ain't no oth-er man but you.
Ain't you.
Bass drum

Candyman

Words & Music by Christina Aguilera & Linda Perry

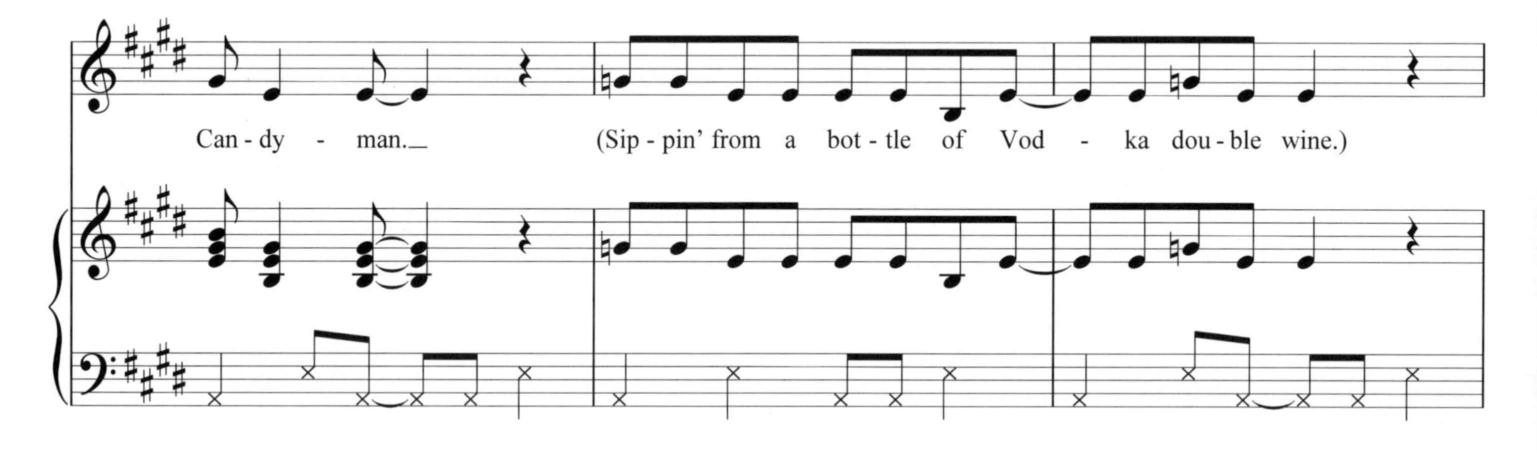

E7
yeah.
1. I met him out for din-ner on a
(2.) took me to the Spi-der Club at
(3.) Well by now I'm get-ting all
Fri-day night, he real-ly had me work-in' up an ap-pe-tite. He
Hol-ly-wood and Vine. We drank cham-pagne and we danced all night. We
both-ered and hot. When he kissed my mouth he real-ly hit the spot. He had
A7
E
had tat-toos up and down his arm. There's no-thing more dan-gerous than a
shook the pa-pa-raz-zi for a big sur-prise. The gos-sip to-night will be to-
lips like su-gar cane. Good things come for

B7
A7
To Coda
boy with charm.__ He's a one-stop shop,_ makes the pan-ties drop._
mor-row's head-lines. He's a one-stop shop,_ makes my cher-ry pop._ He's a
boys who wait.__
E7
sweet talk-ing su-gar coat-ed can-dy - man.__ A sweet talk-ing su-gar coat-ed
1.
can-dy - man._ Oh, yeah.
2.
N.C.
2. He Vocal ad lib.
Drums

Ba - bow.
Hey, yeah.
Yeah,
A7
E7
yeah.
Oh yeah, yeah, sweet on down. He's a
B7
A7
E7
one-stop shop, makes my cher - ry pop. He's a sweet talk - ing su - gar coat - ed
Drums
D.S. al Coda
can - dy - man. A sweet talk - ing su - gar coat - ed can - dy - man.

Coda
N.C.
(Tar-zan and Jane were swing - ing on a vine.) Can-dy-man._ Can-dy-man._
Drums
(Sip-pin' from a bot-tle of Vod - ka dou-ble wine.) Can-dy-man._ Can-dy-man._
N.C.
Sweet su-gar. Can-dy-man._ He's a one-stop, got-cha hot, mak-in' all the pan-ties drop.
Sweet su-gar. Can-dy-man._ He's a one-stop, got me hot, mak-in' my "ah" hot.
Sweet su-gar. Can-dy-man._ He's a one stop, get it well it's hot, ba-by don't stop.

A7
Sweet su-gar. He got those lips like su-gar cane.
E
B7
Good things come for boys who wait. He's a one-stop shop with a
A7
E7
real big "ah." He's a sweet talk-ing su-gar coat-ed can-dy - man. A
sweet talk-ing su-gar coat-ed can-dy - man. A can-dy - man.
1.
2.

E7
Vocal ad lib.
Can-dy - man.
Can-dy - man.
N.C.
(Can-dy - man.)
(Can-dy - man.)
(Can-dy - man.)
(Can-dy - man.)
N.C.
(Tar-zan and Jane were swing-
- ing on a vine.)
(Chorus) (Tar-zan and Jane were swing - ing on a vine.)

(Sip - pin' from a bot - tle of Vod - ka dou - ble wine.) (Chorus) (Sip - pin' from a bot - tle of Vod -
- ka dou - ble wine.) (Jane lost her grip and a - down she fell.)
(Chorus)(Jane lost her grip and a - down she fell.) (Squared her - self a - way as she
let out a yell.) (Chorus)(Squared her - self a - way as she let out a yell.)

Can't Hold Us Down

Words & Music by Christina Aguilera, Scott Storch,
Matthew Wilder, Gregory Prestopino & Matt Morris

Fm
When a fe-male fires back, sud - den-ly big talk-er don't know how to act. So,
If you look back at his-to-ry, it's a com-mon dou-ble stan-dard of so-ci-e-ty: The
Cm
he does what an-y lit-tle boy would do, mak - ing up a few false ru-mors or two.
guy gets all the glo-ry the more he can score, while the girl can do the same and yet you call her a whore.
Fm
That for sure is not a man to me, slan-der-ing names for pop-u-lar-i-ty. It's
I don't un-der-stand why it's O.-K.; the guy can get a-way with it, the girl gets named.
Cm
sad you on-ly get your fame through con-tro-ver-sy. But now it's time for me to come and give you more to say.
All my la-dies, come to-geth-er and make a change and start a new be-gin-ning for us; ev-'ry-bod-y sing.

This is for my girls all a - round the world who have come a - cross a man that don't re - spect your worth,
A♭
4fr
think-ing all wom - en should be seen, not heard. So what do we do, girls? Shout out loud! We're
Cm
3fr
let - tin' 'em know we're gon - na stand our ground, so lift your hands high - er and wave 'em proud.
A♭
4fr
1
Take a deep breath and say it loud: Nev - er can, nev - er will, can't hold us down!

Cm
3fr
No - bod - y hold us down. No - bod - y hold us
(Gon - na hold us down.) (Gon - na hold us down.)
A♭
4fr
down. No - bod - y hold us down. Nev - er can, nev - er will. So,
(Gon - na hold _ us down.)
2
N.C.
can, nev - er will, can't hold us down! Here's some - thin' I just can't un - der - stand: if a
3
guy have three _ girls, then he's the man. _ He can e - ven give us some head and sex or roar; _ if a

girl do the same, then she's a whore. But the ta - ble's 'bout to turn, I bet my fame on it. Cats
take my i - deas and put their name on it. It's al - right, though; you can't hold me down. I
Fm
got to keep on mov - ing. Tell my girls with a man who be try'n' the knack: Do it
8va
(8va)
Cm
right back to him, and let that be that. You need to let him know that his name is whack, and Lit - tle
8va

You're just a lit - tle boy; think you're so
Kim and Chris - ti - na A - gui - le - ra got the phat.
(8va)
Ab
4fr
cute, so coy.
You must talk so big to make
Cm
3fr
up for small - er things. You're just a lit - tle boy; all you do
Ab
4fr
is an - noy. You must talk so big to make up for small - er things.
(This is for my

Cm
3fr
(1st time only)
This is for my girls all a - round the world who have come a - cross a man that don't re - spect your worth,
girls.)
(Continue vocal ad lib.)
3
3
A♭
4fr
think-ing all wom - en should be seen, not heard. So what do we do, girls? Shout out loud! We're
Cm
3fr
let - tin' 'em know we're gon - na stand our ground, so lift your hands high - er and wave 'em proud.
3
3
A♭
4fr
1
Take a deep breath and say it loud: Nev - er can, nev - er will, can't hold us down!

2
N.C.
can, nev - er will, can't hold us down! (1st time only)
Spread the word:
Repeat and Fade
Can't hold us down!
Optional Ending
Can't hold us down!

Car Wash

Words & Music by Norman Whitfield

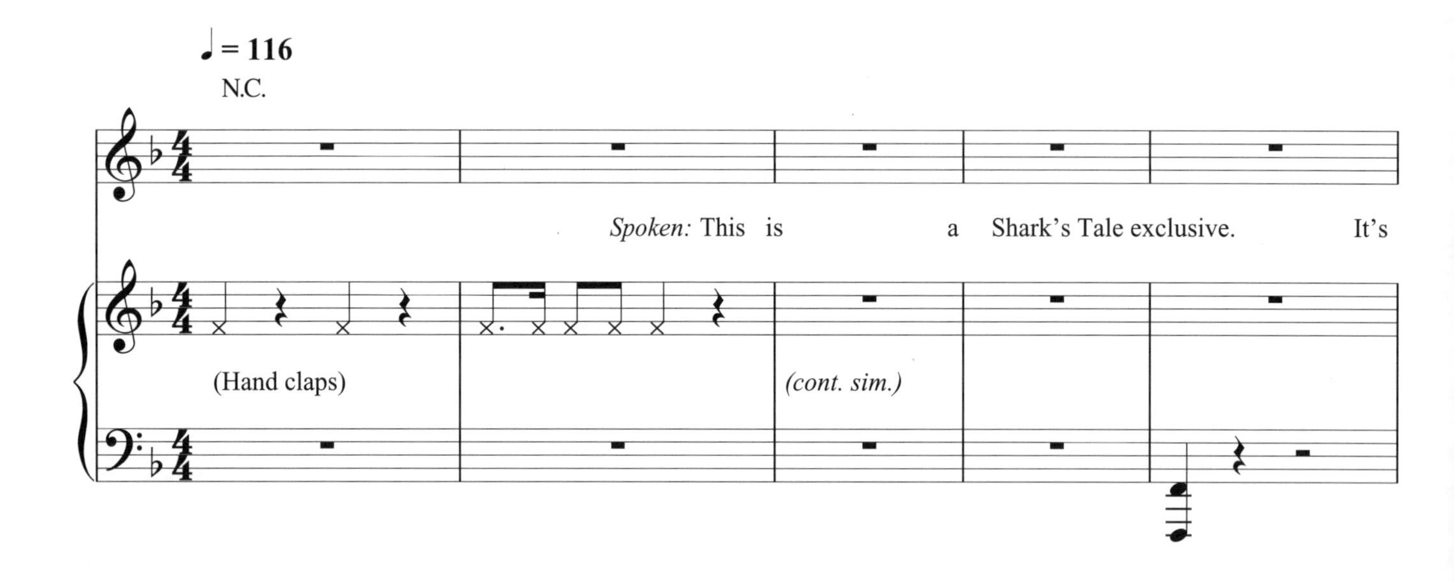

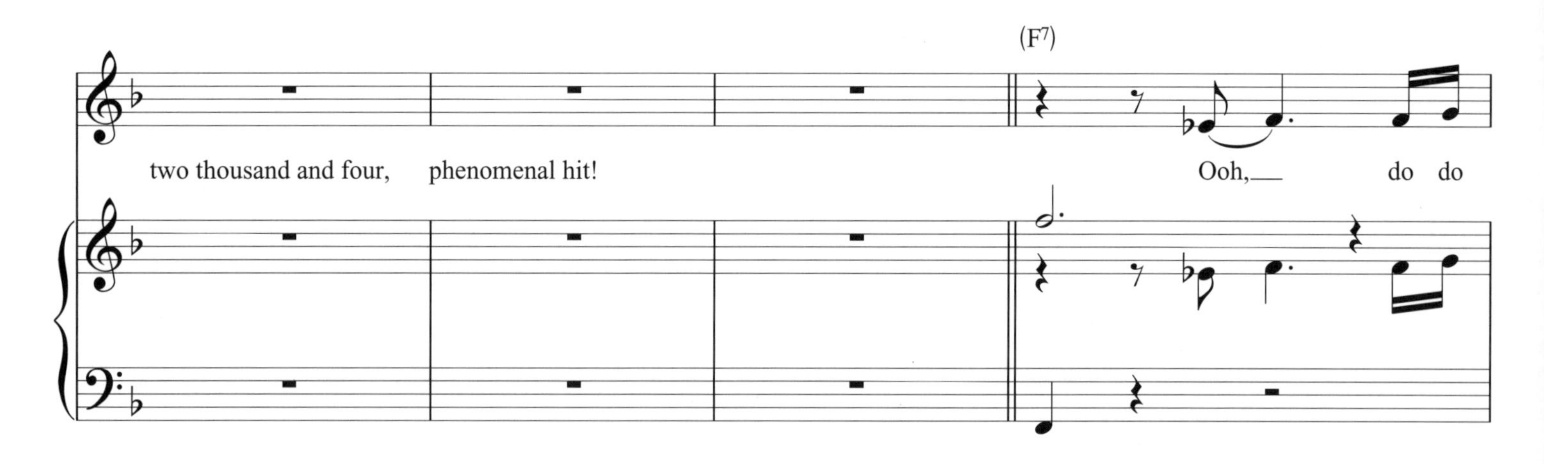

Ooh, do do do do do do do.
Car wash, car
wash.
Ooh,
do do do do do do.
F7
Na na na na na
ooh.
Ooh,
do do do do do do.
Na na na na na
ooh.

F7
1. You might not ev - er get rich;
2. Come sum-mer the work gets kind of hard.
let me tell you it's bet-ter than dig-ging a ditch.
This ain't no place to be if you're plan-ning on be-ing a star.
There ain't no tell - ing who you might meet,
Let me tell you it's al - ways cool;
and the
a mo-vie star or may-be a com - mon thief,
boss don't mind some - times if you're act - ing like a fool,
work - ing at the

(D) (E♭) (E) (F) (D) (E♭) (E) (F) (D) (E♭) (E)
car - wash,
at the car - wash, yeah;
(F) (D) (E♭) (E) (F) (D) (E♭) (E) (F) (D) (E♭) (E)
at the car - wash,
work-ing at the
(F) (D) (E♭) (E)
1.
N.C.
2.
N.C.
car - wash, yeah.
Said, said, said...
F
(Work and work.) Well, those cars nev - er stop com-ing (Work and work.) Keep

these rags and ma - chines hum - ming. (Work and work.) My
fing - ers to the bones. (Work and work.)
Keep on, I can't wait till it's time to go home.
B♭maj7
Am7
Gm7
6fr
5fr
3fr
Hey, get your car washed to - day.
Fill up,
and you don't have to pay, yeah.
Hey, get your

B♭
N.C.
(F)
car washed to - day.
Give it up
right a - way!
(Car - wash.)
Spoken: Sharks in the water make their
jaws lock. When I swim through the grim, I'm too hot. Y'all can make your bets, y'all small tuna fish; I'm one big catch. (You
shark
slay - er!)
Bow down, player, 'cause
this right here will be your worst nightmare.
Work that, work that, pop back, hurt that. Turn this up and bring it all up on the surface.
Nine to

five I gotta keep that fat stack coming.
No matter how
big the shark is, the right keep running.
Washing
cars ain't no place to be a superstar, man.
That's why I
work
and
work.
Work-ing
at
the
(F)
(D)
(E♭)
(E)
car
-
wash,
at
the
car
-
wash,
yeah;
at
the
car
-
wash,

(F) (D) (E♭) (E) (F) (D) (E♭) (E)
work - ing at the car - wash, yeah. So
N.C.
F7
come on, come on, come on, come on. Ooh,
do do do do do do.
Na na na na na
ooh.
Ooh,

do do do do do do.
Na na na na na
ooh.
B♭maj7
Am7
Gm7
Hey, get your car washed to-day!
B♭maj7
Am7
Gm7
Hey, get your car washed to-day!
B♭maj7
Am7
Gm7
F
Hey, get your car washed to-day!
Spoken: Phe-no-me-nal hit!

Come On Over Baby (All I Want Is You)

Words & Music by Paul Rein, Eric Dawkins, Shelly Peiken, Johan Aberg, Ray Cham, Ron Fair, Guy Rochie & Chaka Blackman

E♭ A♭ B♭7 E♭
1. Hey, boy don't you know I got some-thing go - ing on. Yes I do.
2. I want you to know you could be the one for me. Yes you could.
A♭ B♭7 E♭ A♭ B♭7
All my friends are gon-na come, gon - na par - ty all night long.
You got all I'm look-ing for, you got per-son - a - li - ty.
E♭ A♭ B♭7 E♭ E♭/G
Oh, yeah. I know you know,
Oh. I know you know
A♭ B♭7 E♭ A♭ B♭7
I just want us to go. The fun we'll have, you'll nev-er be a - lone.
I'm gon - na give you more. The things you say, I nev-er felt this way be - fore.

E♭
A♭
B♭7
E♭
E♭/G
6fr
4fr
6fr
6fr
So boy won't you come? We will par - ty till the dawn.
So boy won't you come? Won't you come and op - en the door.
A♭
E♭
A♭
B♭9
N.C.
Lis - ten to me. (All I want is you.) Come ov - er here ba - by. (All I want is
E♭
A♭
B♭7
Cm7
E♭/G
3fr
you.) You make me go cra - zy. (All I want is you.) Now ba - by don't be shy.
A♭
Adim
A♭/B♭
You bet - ter cross the line. I'm gon - na love you right. All I want is you.

E♭
6fr
E♭/G
A♭
4fr
B♭7
6fr
E♭
6fr
Come on ov - er, come on ov - er ba - by. Come on ov - er,
A♭
4fr
B♭7
6fr
E♭
6fr
come on ov - er ba - by. Come on ov - er.
Cm7
3fr
Now ba - by don't be shy.
A♭
4fr
Adim
A♭/B♭
You bet - ter cross the line. I'm gon - na love you right. (All I want is

E♭
A♭
B♭9
you.) Come ov - er here ba - by. (All I want is
Vocal ad lib.
E♭
A♭
B♭7
Cm7
E♭/G
you.) You make me go cra - zy. (All I want is you.) Now ba - by don't be shy.
A♭
Adim
A♭/B♭
You bet - ter cross the line. I'm gon - na love you right. 'Cause
1.
2.
all I want is you. all I want is you. echo
(All I want is

Dirrty

Words & Music by Christina Aguilera, Balewam Muhammed,
Dana Stinson, Reggie Norm & Jasper Cameron

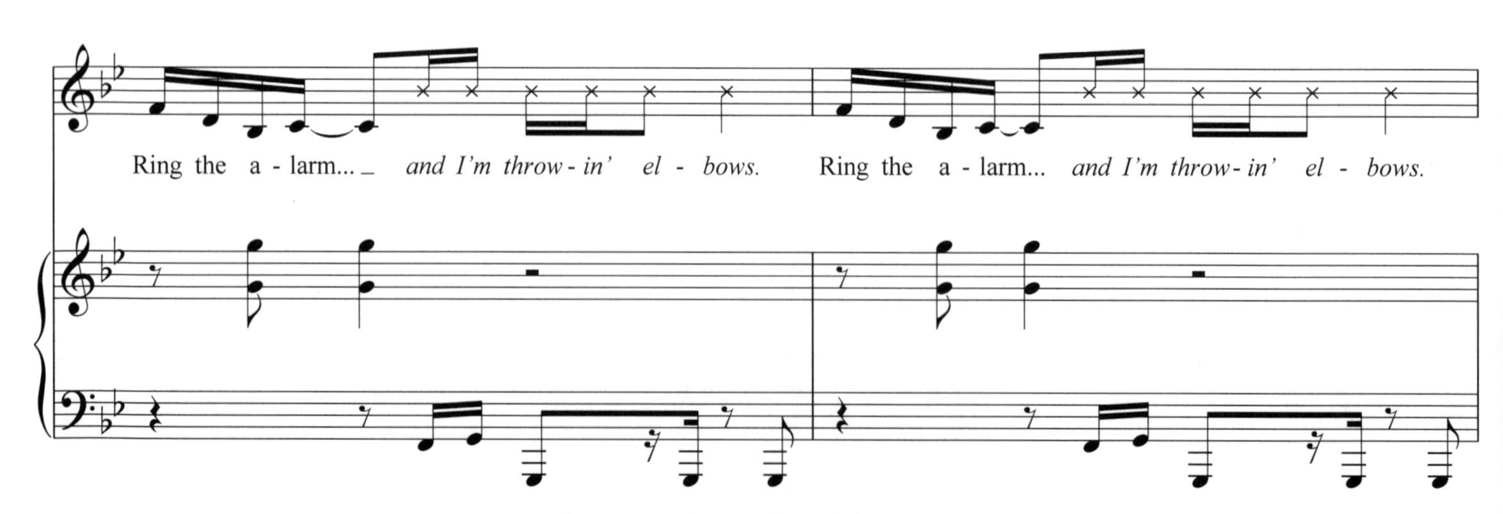

1
2
Ring the a - larm... and I'm throw - in' el - bows.
Uhh... let me loose.
N.C.
Ooh, I'm o - ver - due; gim - me some room, com - in' through.
Ah, heat is up. La - dies fel - las, drop your cups.
Paid my dues; I'm in the mood. Me and my girls come to shake the room.
Bod - ies packed front to back. Move your ass, I like that.
D. J.'s spin - nin', show your hands. Let's get dirr - ty, that's my jam. I
Tight hip - hug - gers, low for sho'. Shake a lit - tle some - thin' on the flo'. I

need that uh to get me off, sweat - in' till my clothes come off.
need that uh to get me off, sweat - in' till my clothes come off.
G5
3fr
It's ex - plo - sive, speak - ers are pump - in'. Still jump - in', six in the morn - in'.
Let's get o - pen, cause a com - mo - tion. Still go - in' eight in the morn - in'.
Ta - ble danc - in', glass - es are crash - in'. No ques - tion, time for some ac - tion.
There's no stop - pin', we keep it pop - pin'. Hard rock - in', ev - 'ry - one's talk - in'.
Tem - per - 'tures up; (Can you feel it?) 'bout to e - rupt. Some one get my
Give all you got; (Give it to me.) just hit the spot. Gon - na get my

N.C.
girls, get your boys, gon - na make some noise.
girls, get your boys, gon - na make some noise.
Gon - na get
G5
3fr
row - dy. Gon - na get a lit - tle un - ru - ly. Get it fired up in a
hur - ry. Wan - na get dirr - ty. It's a - bout time that I came to start the
par - ty. Sweat drip - pin' off o' my bod - y. Danc - in' get - tin' just a lit - tle

1
N.C.
naugh - ty. Wan-na get dirr - ty. It's a-bout time for my ar - ri - val.
2
N.C.
It's a-bout time for my ar - ri - val.
Here it comes, it's the one that you've been wait - in' on. Get
up, get it rough, yup that's what's up. Giv - in' just what you love to the max - i - mum. Uh -
oh, (Uh - oh,) here we go. (here we go.) What to do when the mu - sic starts to drop? That's

when we take it to the park - ing lot, and I bet you, some - bod - y's gon - na call the cops. Uh -

oh, (Uh - oh,) here we go. (here we go.) Oh,

yeah, yeah. Rap: (See additional lyrics)

1
2
G5
3fr
It's gon - na get row - dy. Gon - na get a lit - tle un -
- ru - ly. Get it fired up in a hur - ry. Wan - na get dirr - ty.
It's a - bout time that I came to start the par - ty. Sweat drip - pin' off o' my

Additional Lyrics

Rap: Hot damn! Got the jam, like a summer show.
I keep my pawn lookin' like a crash dummy drove.
My gear look like the bait got my money froze.
But there are presidents I pimp like Teddy Ro'.
Got the one that excites ya deepest,
At the media shine, I'm shinin' with both of the sleeves up.
Yo Christina, what happened here?
My black, live and in color, like Rodman hair.

The club is packed, the bar is filled, they're waitin' for
Sister to act like Lauren Hill. Frankly,
It's so black, no bargain deals, I'll drop a
Four-wheel drive with foreign wheels. Throw it up!
Bet you this is Brick City, you heard o' that.
We're blessed and hung low, like Bernie Mack.
Dogs, let 'em out; women, let 'em in.
It's like I'm O.D.B., that what they're thinkin'.

Fighter

Words & Music by Christina Aguilera & Scott Storch

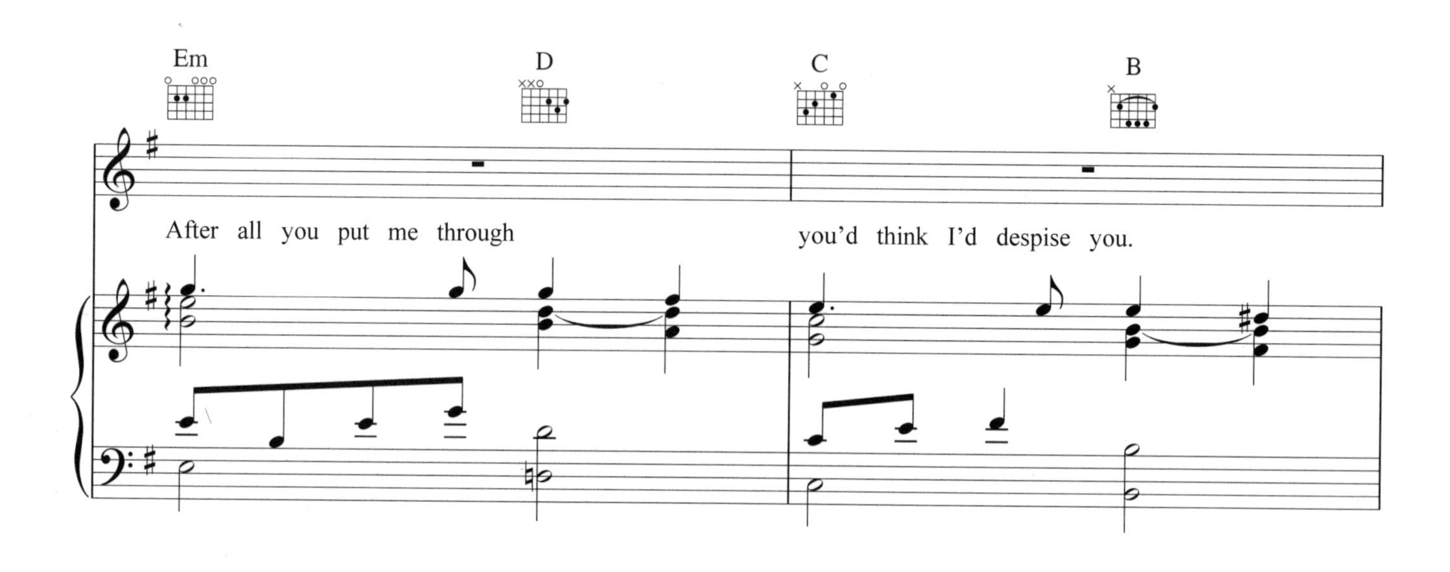

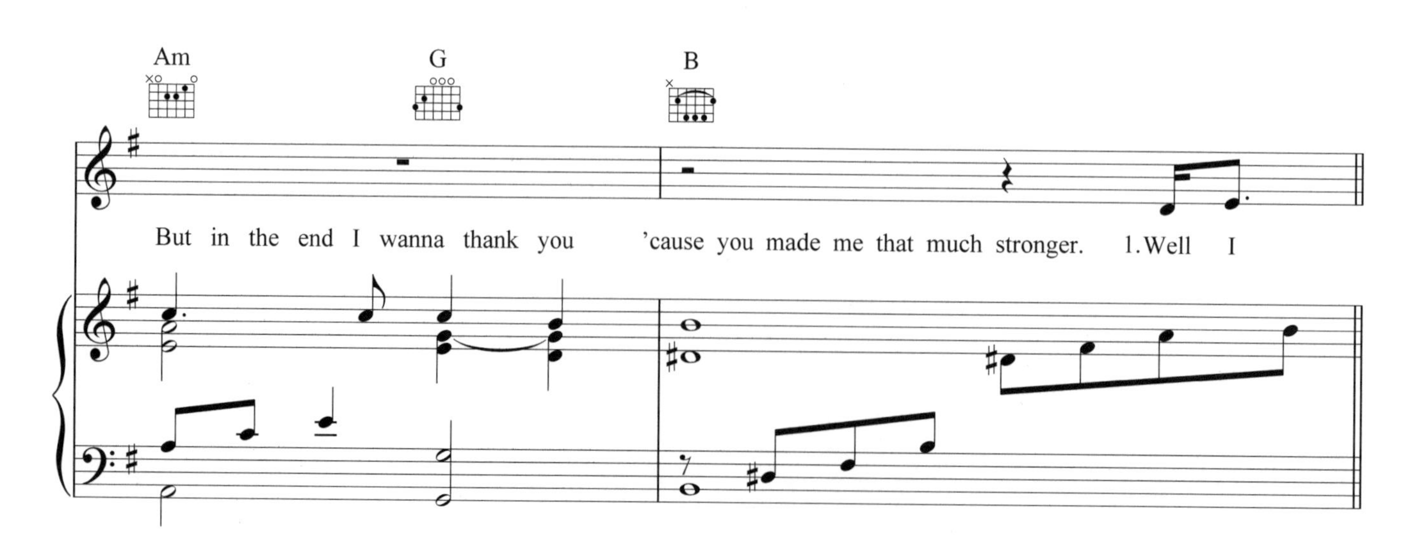

E5 G5 N.C. D5 F5 E5 N.C.
thought I knew you, think - in' that you were true. Guess I,
(2.) saw it com - ing all of your back stab - bing. Just so
E5 G5 N.C. D5 F5 E5
I could - n't trust, called your bluff, time is up 'cause I've had e - nough. You were
you could cash in on a good thing be - fore I'd re - al - ise your game. I heard
G5 N.C. D5 F5 E5 N.C.
there by my side, al - ways down for the ride. But your
you're go - ing round play - in' the vic - tim now. But don't
E5 G5 N.C. D5 F5 E5
joy - ride just came down in flames 'cause you're greed sold me out in shame. Mm.
ev - en be - gin feel - ing I'm the one to blame 'cause you dug your own grave.

A5
Af - ter all of the steal - ing and cheat - ing you pro - bab - ly think that I hold re - sent - ment for
Af - ter all of the fights and the lies 'cause you're want - ing to haunt me. But that don't work a - ny
G5
3fr
E5
N.C.
you. But uh, uh, oh no, you're wrong.
more. No more, uh, uh, it's ov - er.
A5
B5
C5
D5
5fr
'Cause if it was - n't for all that you tried to do I would - n't know just how ca - pa - ble I
'Cause if it was - n't for all of your tor - ture I would - n't know how to be this way now and
am to pull through.
nev - er back down.
So I wan - na say thank - you 'cause it

Em
F#m
G
Am
makes me that much strong - er, makes me work a lit - tle bit hard - er, It
C
B
Am
G
Em
makes me that much wis - er So thanks for mak - ing me a fight - er.
Em
F#m
G
Am
Made me learn a lit - tle bit fast - er, made my skin a lit - tle bit thick - er. It
C
B
Am
G
Em
To Coda
makes me that much smart - er. So thanks for mak - ing me a fight - er.

1.
E5
G5
3fr
D5
5fr
F5
E5
Oh,
oh,
oh,
oh,
N.C.
oh,
eh,
eh,
oh.
Nev - er
2.
Em
D
C
B
Am
G
How could this man I though I knew turn out to be un - just, so cruel. Could on - ly see the good in you,
pre - tend - ed not to see the truth. You tried to hide your lies, dis - guise your - self through liv - ing in de - nial.

Am
G
B
Em
F♯m
But in the end you'll see you won't stop me.
I am a fight - er and I,
(I'm a
D.S. al Coda
G
Am
C
B
Am
G
Em
I ain't gon - na stop.
There is no turn - ing back,
I've had e - nough.
fight - er.)
(I ain't gon - na stop.)
CODA
Em
F♯m
G
Am
Thought I would - n't for - get, thought I,
I re - mem - ber.
C
B
Am
G
Em
Yes, I re - mem - ber.
I re - mem - ber.

Em
F♯m
G
Am
Makes me that much strong - er
makes me work a lit - tle bit hard - er.
It
C
B
Am
G
Em
makes me that much wis - er.
So thanks for mak - ing me a fight - er.
N.C.
Made me learn a lit - tle bit fast - er,
made my skin a lit - tle bit thick - er.
It
makes me that much smart - er.
So thanks for mak - ing me a fight - er.

Genie In A Bottle

Words & Music by Steve Kipner, David Frank & Pamela Sheyne

D♭5
C
F5
E♭5
4fr
- tu - ry ___ of lone - ly nights ___ wait - ing for some - one ___ to re - lease ___
___ more dance _ and then we're _ good to go, wait - ing for some - one ___ who needs ___
D♭5
C
Fm
E♭5
___ me. You're lick - in' your lips _ and blow - in' kiss - es my way. But that ___
___ me. Hor - mones rac - ing at the speed of light. But that ___
D♭5
C
F5
E♭5
___ don't mean _ I'm gon - na give it a - way, ___ ba - by, ba - by ba - by.
___ don't mean _ it's got - ta be to - night, ___ ba - by, ba - by, ba - by.
D♭5
C
Fm
E♭
3fr
D♭
Cm7
Oh. ___ My bod - y's say - ing let's go.

Fm
E♭
D♭
Cm7
3fr
Oh.
But my heart is say-ing no, no.
Fm E♭ D♭ Cm7 Fm E♭
If you wan-na be with me, ba-by, there's a price to pay. I'm a ge-nie in a bot-
D♭ C Fm E♭
-tle; you got-ta rub me the right way. If you wan-na be with
D♭ Cm7
1
Fm E♭
me, I can make your wish come true. You got-ta make a big im-pres-

D♭
C
F5
E♭5
- sion. Got - ta like what you do.
I'm a ge-nie in a bot - tle, ba - by.
D♭5
4fr
C
F5
E♭5
You got - ta rub me the right way, hon - ey.
I'm a ge-nie in a bot - tle, ba - by.
D♭5
4fr
C
2
Fm
E♭5
Come, come, come on and let me out.
true. Just come and set me free,
D♭
C7
F5
E♭5
ba - by, and I'll be with you.
I'm a ge - nie in a bot - tle, ba - by.

Db5
C
F5
Eb5
4fr
You got - ta rub _ me the right way, hon - ey. _
I'm a ge-nie in a bot - tle, ba - by.
Db5
C5
F5
Eb5
4fr
3fr
Come, _ come, come on and let me out.
I'm a ge-nie in a bot - tle, ba - by.
Db5
C7
F5
Eb5
4fr
You got - ta rub _ me the right way, hon - ey.
I'm a ge-nie in a bot - tle, ba - by.
Db5
N.C.
Fm
Eb
4fr
3fr
Come, _ come, come on and let me out.
Oh. _

D♭
Cm7
Fm
E♭
My bod-y's say-ing let's go. Oh.
D♭
Fm
E♭5
But my heart is say-ing no, no. If you wan-na be with
D♭
Cm7
Fm
E♭5
me, ba-by, there's a price to pay. I'm a ge-nie in a bot-
D♭
C
Fm
E♭
-tle. You got-ta rub me the right way. If you wan-na be with

Db
Cm7
3fr
1
Fm
Eb
3fr
me, I can make your wish come true. You got - ta make a big im - pres -
Db
C
F
Eb
3fr
3
- sion. You got - ta like what you do. If you wan - na be with
2
Fm
Eb5
Db
C7
true. Just come and let me free, ba - by, and I'll be with you.
Fm
N.C.
I'm a ge - nie in a bot - tle, ba - by. Come, come, come on and let me out.

Hurt

Words & Music by Christina Aguilera, Linda Perry & Mark Ronson

Am7
B
If on - ly I knew what I know to - day.
And it's so hard to say good - bye when it comes to this.
Em
Ooh, ooh.
Lead Vocal ad lib.
I would
Would you
C
A/C♯
hold you in my arms; I would take the pain a - way,
tell me I was wrong? Would you help me un - der - stand? Are you
D
B7/D♯
thank you for all you've done, for - give all your mis - takes. There's
look - ing down up - on me? Are you proud of who I am? There's

C
A/C♯
noth-ing I would-n't do to hear your voice a-gain. Some-
noth-ing I would-n't do to have just one more chance, to
D
B7/D♯
times I wan-na call you, but I know you won't be there.
look in-to your eyes and see you look-ing back.
Em
B/D♯
4fr
Whoa, I'm sor-ry for blam-ing you
Em
C
3
for ev-'ry-thing I just could-n't do;

Am
1
B
and I've hurt my - self by hurt - ing
Em
2
B
you. Some days I feel broke self, oh.
Em
Em/D
Cmaj7
If I had just one more day, I would
Em
Em/D
Cmaj7
tell you how much that I've missed you since you've been a - way.

Am
E/G#
Oh, it's dan - ger - ous, it's so out of
Am/G
F#m7b5(b9)
3fr
line to try and turn back
B
time.
Em
B/D#
4fr
I'm sor - ry for blam - ing you

Em
C
for ev - 'ry - thing
I just could - n't do;
Am
B
and I've hurt my - self...
C
Am7
B
Em
N.C.
by hurt - ing you.

Infatuation

Words & Music by Christina Aguilera, Scott Storch & Matt Morris

Original key G♯ minor.

Am
Dm
far a - way.
Intrigues me with ev - 'ry move till I'm
with - in.
Feels so good it must be a sin. I can't
E7
Am
Dm
breath-less, I'm help-less, can't keep my cool.
Steals my heart when he takes my hand
stop what I start-ed, I'm giv-ing in.
He brings light to my fan - ta - sies,
E7
Am
and we dance to the rhy-thm of the band.
I feel his fin - ger - tips
sparks a pas - sion in - side of me.
Finds the words when I
Dm
E7
grip my hips and I slip as we dip in - to a state of bliss.
can - not speak. In the si - lence his heart beat is mu - sic to me.

Dm
E7
Am
Ma - ma used to warn me to be - ware those la - tin lov -
Ma - ma used to warn me not to rush love with a - no -
Dm
E7
- ers. She said, "I gave my heart too soon and that's how I
- ther. She said, "I'm not try - ing to lec - ture, I just care
Am
Dm
be - came your Mo - ther." I said "Ay, Ma - ma, you seem to
a - bout my daugh - ter." "Ay, Ma - ma, you seem to
E7
Am
for - get, I'm not in love yet. Sweet talk don't win me ov - er."
for - get, I nev - er will let a man con - trol my e - mo - tions."

Dm7
E7
But I re - al- ise big brown eyes can hip - no - tize
But when he smiles I feel like a lit - tle child
when he says…
Am
Dm
E7
I am For - blei Mo - ri - qua, read the tat - too on his arm.
Am
Dm
E7
He tells me, "Ma - mi, I need ya." And my heart - beat pumps so strong.
Am
Dm
E7
Get - ting lost in a rit - mo he whis - pers, "Te quie - ro." "Te quie ro."
3
3
3

Am
Dm
E7
To Coda
I be-gin to give in with no he - si-ta - tion. Can't help my in - fa - tu-
Am
Dm
E7
-a - tion. (Ah.) It's pure in - fa - tu-
Am
Dm
E7
-a - tion. Ah.
F
C7
Caught be-tween my Ma-ma's words and what I feel in - side.

F
E7
Want-ing to ex-plore his world but part of me wants to hide.
F
E7
Should I risk it, can't re-sist it, this has caught me by sur-prise. Should I
F
G
E7/G#
let him take me to Puer-to Ri-co? I can't hold back no more. Let's got to-
Am
Dm7
E
night.

Am
Dm7
E
Vocal ad lib.
Am
Dm7
Pa - pi hold me, say that you a - dore me.
E
Am
Nev - er let go, nev - er leave me lone - ly. Pa - pi hold me, say
Dm7
E
D.S. al Coda
that you a - dore me. Nev - er let go, nev - er leave me lone - ly.

Coda
Am
Dm
help my in - fa - tu - a - tion.
(Ah.)
E7
Am
It's pure in - fa - tu - a - tion.
1.
Dm
E7
(Ah.)
Can't help in - fa - tu - a -
2.
Dm
E7
N.C.
Hey.

Makes Me Wanna Pray

Words & Music by Christina Aguilera, Steve Winwood, Kara Dioguardi & Rich Harrison

- be - lief. Is this real - ly me, ha, in the mir-ror I see, star-ing back at me?
F♯m7
3
Could it be a new re-flec-tion of a wo-man com-plete?_
1. All of a sud-den I'm so con -
2. I've kept some com-pa - ny I should-
Drums
- free, yeah. (Well al - right.) Your lov-ing's do - ing some-thing strange__ to__ me. (Well al - right.)
- n't have. (Well al - right.) Made some mis- takes_ but that's in_____ the_past. I'm pro -
Got a new_ flame, ha, have - n't been the same. Some-thing in me's changed, re - ar-ranged_ and I
-fess-ing here_ to you, proof that I am through. I'm com-ing clean, now I can breath and I

F♯m7
feel that I've been saved.
fi - nal - ly be - lieve.
You got me feel - ing like you're that some - thing I've been miss - ing.
You got me think - ing I'll be al - right and you're the rea - son.
Ev - 'ry - thing's hea - ven 'cause life with you has been a bless - ing.
Ooh, I can feel it, we're mov - ing in a new di - rect - ion.
(Ooh ooh ooh ooh.) I got it bad in a se - ri - ous way.
(Ooh ooh ooh ooh) Your love has brought me to a high - er place.

(Who knew, who knew?) It be you to re-store my faith. Ev-er-y day
I'm a-mazed and it makes me wan-na get down and pray.
B6/F♯
F♯m7
B6/F♯
Makes me wan-na get down and pray. Said it
To Coda
1.
F♯m
makes me wan-na get down and pray.
Yeah.
5

2.
F♯m
B6/F♯
Makes me wan - na get down and pray.
Makes me wan - na get down and pray.
8vb
Where would I be, where would I be with - out you by my side?
Where would I be, where would I be with - out you stand - ing by? Makes me wan -

-na (pray), makes me need to (pray). When I'm
D.S. al Coda
feel-ing low and all a-lone, you're the light in my day. Yeah!
Coda
F♯m
B6/F♯
(Pray, pray.)
Vocal ad lib.
Play 3 times ad lib.
That's it!

Mercy On Me

Words & Music by Christina Aguilera & Linda Perry

Am
please.
Am
Adim
Am
Vocal ad lib.
Adim

Am
Je - sus, I must con - fess
Dm
that in all my lone - li - ness I've for -
Am
E7
-sak - en and I've sinned, leav - ing frag - ments of a man so bro -
Am
N.C.
- ken. I could tell you what I've

Am
done,
(2.) grace.
3. Instrumental
or should I tell you where
In my weak - ness I've
Dm
I went wrong?
lost faith.
Well, the more that I start to
I've been care- less and I've been
Am
E7
play my de-ceipt - ful ev - il ways keep a - grow - ing strong - er
warned, and the de - vil in - side me is torn, God bless the man that I
Am
N.C.
by the day.
have scorned.
Oh, Lord have mer - cy on

Am
— my — soul, —
for I have walked a sin -
.mer - cy on — my soul.
Oh, I'm
Dm
- - ful road. —
So I'm
beg - ging I'm plead - ing I'm need - ing I want you to know. —
Am
To Coda II
E7
N.C.
gon - na get down on my knees, beg for - give-ness to help set me free. — Lord have
So I'm down up - on my knees. — Oh,
Am
To Coda I
1.
mer - cy — on me please. —
2. Mo - ther Ma - ry, — full of

2.
D.S. al Coda I
Coda I
Adim
So don't let me
Am
fool a-round no more.
Send your an - gels down to
Dm
get me through that door.
Well, I've gone and con-fessed my re -
Am
E7
-grets, and I pray I'm not held in con - tempt.
I'm so lost and I

Am
D.S.S. al Coda II
need you to help me re - pent.
Oh, Lord have
Coda II
E7
Free time
N.C.
Lord. I need for - give - ness.
I need for - give - ness
Am
from you.
Adim
Am

Nobody Wants To Be Lonely

Words & Music by Desmond Child, Gary Burr & Victoria Shaw

N.C.
There you are in a dark-ened room. And you're all a-lone look-ing
Am G
out the win-dow. Your heart is cold and lost the will to love
Dm9 F E F
like a bro-ken ar-row. Here I stand in the
C F G
shad-ows. Come to me, come to me. Both: Can't you see that,

Am
G
Dm9
No - bod - y wants to be lone - ly.
No - bod - y wants to cry.
F
Am
G
My bod - y's long - ing to hold you
Dm9
F
C5
3 fr
so bad it hurts in - side.
Time is pre-cious and it's
G/B
Dm
F
slip-ping a - way and I've been wait-ing for you all of my life.

Am
G
To Coda
No - bod - y wants to be lone - ly. Male: So
Dm9
C/E
F
Am
why,
why don't you let me love you? (Why?)
G
Dm7
F
E
(Why?)
(Why?)
Female: Can you
Am
G
hear my voice?
Do you hear my song?
It's a
3
3

Fmaj7
G
ser - e - nade so your heart can find me, ooh.
Am
G
And sud - den - ly you're fly - ing down the stairs
F
E
in - to my arms ba - by, ooh.
F
C
Male: Be - fore I start go - ing cra - zy

D.S. al Coda
F
G
run to me, Female: run to me Both: 'cause I'm dy - ing.
CODA
Dm9
C/E
F
why, Female: why, why don't you let me love
Fmaj7
C/E
you? Male: I wan-na feel you near me just like the
Am
air you're breath - ing. Female: I need you

Gsus
3 fr
here in my life. Both: Don't walk a - way Female: Don't walk a - way. Male: Don't
G
Fmaj7
walk a - way, walk a - way no, no. Female: No - bod - y wants to be lone - ly.
Dm9
F
Both: No - bod - y wants to cry.
Am
G
No - bod - y wants to be lone - ly.

Dm9
F
No - bod - y wants to cry.
Am
G
My bod - y's long - ing to hold you
Dm9
F
so bad it hurts in - side.
C5
3 fr
G/B
Time is pre - cious and it's slip - ping a - way and I've been

Dm
F
wait - ing for you all of my life.
Am
G
No - bod - y wants to be lone - ly. Male: So
Dm9
C/E
F
why, why, why don't you let me love
Repeat and Fade
Optional Ending
Am
Am
you? Both: No - bod - y wants you?

The Voice Within

Words & Music by Christina Aguilera & Glen Ballard

Csus2
3fr
Dsus
fly. Ooh. When you're
day. Ooh. Now, in a
Em
D/C
C
Gsus2
Dsus
safe in - side your room, you tend to dream of a
world where in - no - cence is quick - ly claimed, it's so
Em
D/C
C
Gsus2
Dsus
place where noth - ing's hard - er than it seems. No one
hard to stand your ground when you're so a - fraid; no one
Em
D/C
C
G/B
Dsus
ev - er wants or both - ers to ex - plain of the
reach - es out a hand for you to hold. When you

Em
D/C
C
Am
D7sus
heart - ache life can bring and what it means.
look out - side, look in - side to your soul.
When there's
cresc.
G
Am7♭5/G
Em/G
G9
A9
4fr
9fr
5fr
no one else, look in - side your - self;
like your old - est friend, just
mf
Am7♭5/E♭
D7sus
G
Am7♭5/G
Em/G
G9
trust the voice with - in.
Then you'll find the strength that will guide your way if
A9
1
Am7♭5/E♭
D7sus
G5
3fr
you'll learn to be - gin to trust the voice with - in.
dim.
mp

2
Am7♭5/E♭
D7sus
Em
B7/F♯
trust the voice with - in.
p
Em/G
A7
Em
B7/F♯
(Ooh, ooh,
sim.
Em/G
A7
Em
B7/F♯
ooh, ooh.)
Life is a jour - ney; it can
f
Em/G
A7
Em
B7/F♯
take you an - y - where you choose to go.
As long as you're learn - ing, you'll find

Em/G
A7
Em
B7/F♯
all you'll ev - er need to know.
Take it, you'll make it.
(Be strong, hold on. Be
Em/G
A7
Cmaj7
Just don't for - sake it be - cause...
no one can
strong; hold on.)
(No one can tell you what you can't do; no one can
B7♯5
N.C.
A
Bm7♭5/A
stop you. You know that I'm talk-ing to you.
When there's no one else, look in-
stop you.)
f
F♯m/A
A9
5fr
B9
Bm7♭5/F
3fr
E7sus
side your - self; like your old - est friend, just trust the voice with-in,
Then you'll

A
Bm7♭5/A
F♯m/A
A9
5fr
B9
find the strength that will guide your way if you'll learn to be-gin to
Bm7♭5/F
3fr
E7sus
A5
5fr
trust the voice with - in.
mp
Young girl, don't cry; I'll be right here when your world starts to fall.
Dsus2
Esus
A(add2)
Ooh, mm.
rit.

What A Girl Wants

Words & Music by Shelly Peiken & Guy Roche

Em7 7fr
Am 5fr
Em7 7fr
Am 5fr
-ed so pa-tient-ly___ while I got it to-geth-er.___ Huh, while I fig-ured it out,_
hide it all from you. But ba-by you knew me bet-ter than I knew my-
Em7 7fr
Am 5fr
Em7 7fr
Am 5fr
___ yeah, yeah. I on-ly looked but I ne-ver touched, 'cos in my heart was a
-self. Love, you... say if you love some-thing let it go, and if it comes back, it's
Dm9 3fr
G11
pic-ture of___ us: hold-ing hands, mak-ing plans and it's luck-y for me__ you un-
yours, that's how you know it's for keeps, yeah, it's for sure, and you're read-y and will-ing to give
C 8fr
Cmaj7 8fr
C7 8fr
Fmaj7 8fr
-der-stand__
me more than
what a girl wants, what a girl needs, what-ev-er makes__ me hap-py__ sets__

Fm7
8fr
B♭11
4fr
C
8fr
you free and I'm thank-ing you for know-ing ex-act-ly what a girl wants,
Cmaj7
8fr
C7
8fr
Fmaj7
8fr
Fm7
8fr
what a girl needs, what-ev-er keeps me in your arms, and I'm thank-ing you for
1. B♭11
4fr
N.C.
Am
5fr
Em7
7fr
Am
5fr
(What I want is what you got, and what you got is what I want.)
Em7
7fr
N.C.
2. B♭maj7
6fr
Am7
5fr
C13
8fr
2. There was a giv-ing it to me, yeah. (What a girl wants, what a girl needs.)

Fmaj9
B♭11
Am7
C13
Somebody sensitive, courageous, sexy, cool and like you. (What a girl wants, what a girl needs,
woh, oh yeah!) (What a girl wants, what a girl needs.)
B♭9
Dm7
You let a girl know how much you care about her I swear, you're the
Eaug
N.C.
one who always knew, you knew, you knew, you knew, you knew.

Ooh, oh, I'm thank-ing you for be-ing here
for me.
What a girl wants, what a girl needs, what-ev-er keeps me in your arms.)
What ev-er keeps
me in your arms is what I need
Lead vocal cont. ad lib.
(What a girl wants, what a girl needs, what-ev-er makes
C
Cmaj7
C7
8fr
me hap-py sets you free and I'm thank-ing you
for know-ing ex-act-ly.
for giv-ing it to me.
Fmaj7
Fm7
B♭11
4fr

1.
C
8fr
Cmaj7
C7
What a girl wants, what a girl needs, what - ev - er keeps me in
Fmaj7
Fm7
B♭11
4fr
your arms, and I'm thank - ing you for giv - ing it. What a girl...)
2.
Am7
5fr
C13
Fmaj9
7fr
Repeat to fade

Walk Away

Words & Music by Christina Aguilera, Scott Storch & Matt Morris

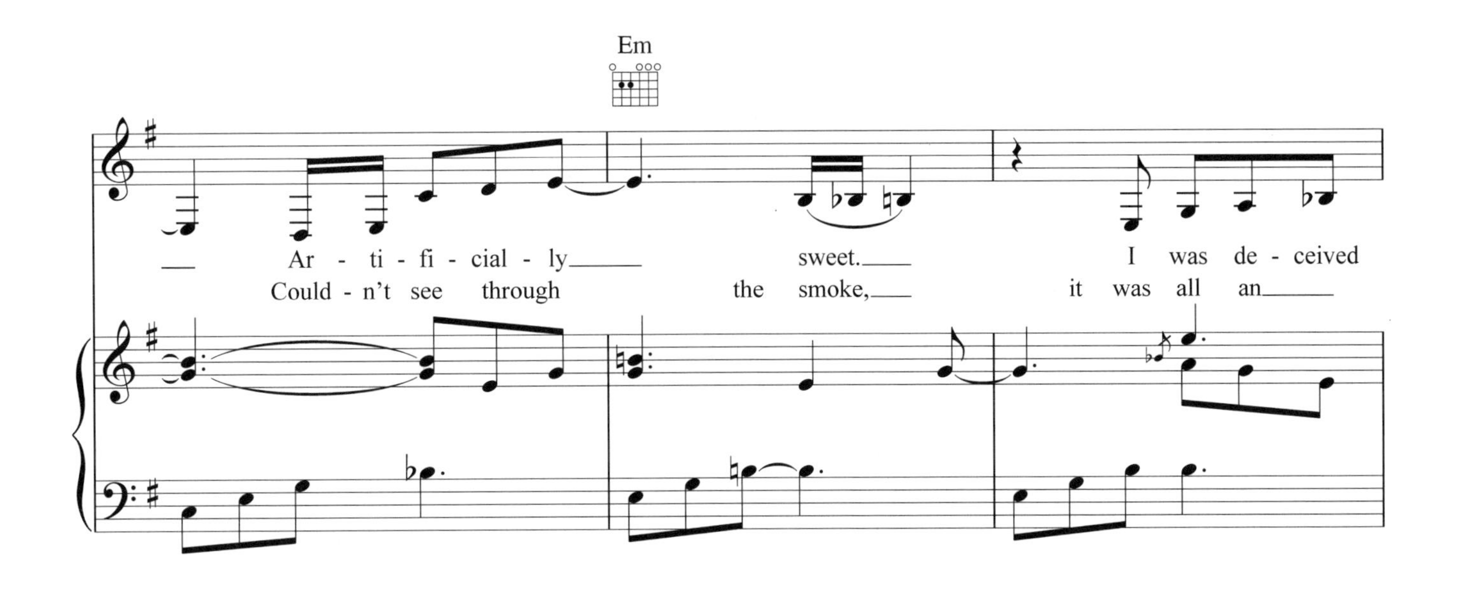
Em
Ar - ti - fi - cial - ly sweet. I was de - ceived
Could - n't see through the smoke, it was all an

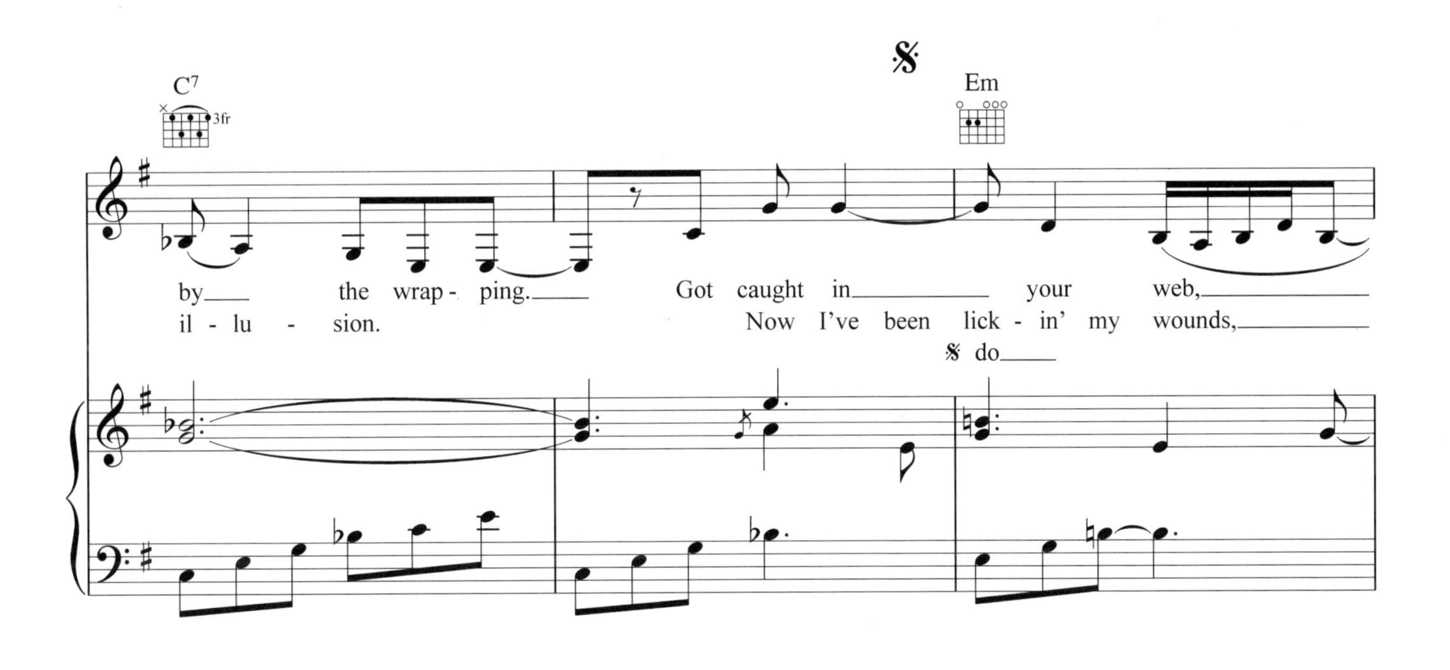
C7
3fr
Em
by the wrap - ping. Got caught in your web,
il - lu - sion. Now I've been lick - in' my wounds,
do

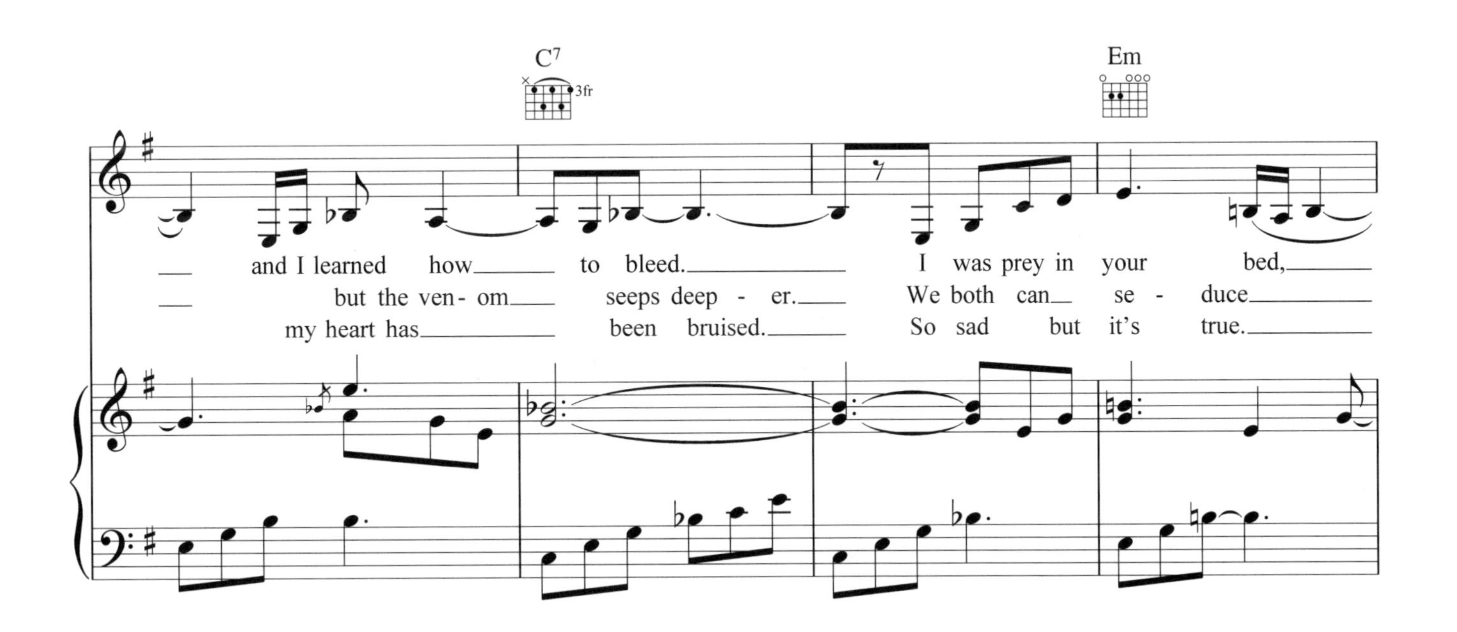
C7
3fr
Em
and I learned how to bleed. I was prey in your bed,
but the ven - om seeps deep - er. We both can se - duce
my heart has been bruised. So sad but it's true.

C7
3fr
and de - voured complete - ly.
but darl - in' you hold me pris - oner.
Each beat re - minds me of you.
Oh, and it
Oh, I'm a -
Em
G
Am
hurts my soul 'cause I can't let go, all these walls are cav - ing in. I can't
- bout to break, I can't stop this ache. I'm ad - dic - ted to your al - lure and I'm
C
Em
G
stop my suf - fer - ing. I hate to show that I've lost con - trol 'cause I,
fiend - in' for a cure. Ev - 'ry step I take leads to one mis - take.
Am
To Coda I
C
I keep go - in' right back to the one thing that I need to
I keep go - in' right back to the one thing that I need.

1.
Em
walk a - way from.
Yeah.
C7
3fr
Em
I need to get a - way from you.
C7
3fr
Need to walk a - way from you. Get a - way, walk a - way, walk a - way.
2. I
2.
Em
G
Am
I can't mend this torn state I'm in. Get - ting no - thing in re - turn. What did

C
Em
G
I do to de-serve the pain of this slow burn. And ev-'ry-where I turn
Am
C
To Coda II
Em
I keep go-in' right back to the one thing that I need to walk a-way from.
C7
3fr
Yeah.
(Need to get a-way from you. Need to walk a-way from you.)
B7
B7/A
2fr
B7/G
Ev-'ry time I try to grasp for air, I am smo-thered in des-pair, it's nev-er

Em
B9
Em
B7
ov - er, ov - er. Oh. It seems I'll nev - er wake from this night - mare.
B7/A
2fr
B7/G
Em
B9
I let out a si - lent prayer, let it be ov - er, ov - er.
Em
Am7
Oh. In - side I'm scream - ing,
Am7/G
B
D.S. al Coda I
beg - ging, plead - ing no more. Now what to

Coda I
C
Em
G
one_thing that I_need. Oh, I'm a-bout to break_ and I can't stop this ache. I'm ad-
Am
C
Em
-dic-ted to your al-lure and I'm_ fiend-in' for_ a cure._ Now_ ev-'ry step_ I take
G
Am
C
D.S.S. al Coda II
leads to one_mis-take I keep go-ing right back to the one_thing that I_need. Oh,
Coda II
Em
C7
3fr
Repeat ad lib. to fade
walk a-way from._ Yeah._

When You Put Your Hands On Me

Words & Music by Robin Thicke & James Gass

Fmaj7
E7
Am
Am/G
Ooh.
I don't know, div-ing out of the sky or liv-
Ooh.
I don't know how to be what you like and simply
B♭/C
Fmaj7
E7
Dm7
-ing like the dia-monds and pearls.
Mm.
See, I have-n't danced to a mu-
op-en up the depths of my soul.
So I keep my wings and my eyes
Am
Dm7
Am
-si-cal tune
and I have-n't no-ticed the flow-ers in bloom.
And
on the down,
rea-dy for no-thing but hold-ing my ground.
And
Dm7
Am
Am/G
Fmaj7
I have-n't smiled when a-lone in my room ve-ry much.
I have-n't used a par-ti-cu-lar noun ve-ry much.
Then

E7
Am
we touched_ oh.
I just know_ when you put_
Cmaj7
Fmaj7
E7
_ your hands on me I feel sex - y.
And my bo - dy turns to gold._
Am
Cmaj7
I just know_ when you put_ your hands on me I feel rea -
B♭/C
E7
Am
- dy.
And I lose my self con - trol.
When you

1.
Am/G
Fmaj7
E7
put your hands on me. Ooh ah.
2.
E7
C♯m
4fr
D
ah. I don't no - tice or pay you no mind.
gliss.
F♯m
C♯/G♯
4fr
Boy, I could - n't care less what you do with your time.
D
A/C♯
Your fin - ger - tips on my hips just move

4 5 6 7 8 9
11/09 (172222)